# The Fabian Society

The Fabian Society has played a central role for more than a century in the development of political ideas and public policy on the left of centre. Analysing the key challenges facing the UK and the rest of the industrialised world in a changing society and global economy, the Society's programme aims to explore the political ideas and the policy reforms which will define progressive politics in the new century.

The Society is unique among think tanks in being a democratically-constituted membership organisation. It is affiliated to the Labour Party but is editorially and organisationally independent. Through its publications, seminars and conferences, the Society provides an arena for open-minded public debate.

Fabian Society
11 Dartmouth Street
London SW1H 9BN
www.fabian-society.org.uk

 Fabian ideas
Series editor: Ellie Levenson

First published December 2002

ISBN 0 7163 0605 0
ISSN 1469 0136

British Library Cataloguing in Publication data.
A catalogue record for this book is available from the British Library.


Printed by Bell & Bain Limited, Glasgow


This pamphlet is kindly supported by

# Contents

# About the authors

Ray Robinson is Professor of Health Policy at the London School of Economics and a Senior Fellow with the European Observatory on Health Care Systems. Earlier in his career he was Director of the Institute for Health Policy Studies at the University of Southampton, Deputy Director of the King's Fund Institute and an economist in HM Treasury. He was also vice-chair of East Sussex Health Authority in the early 1990s and is currently the independent chair of a major clinical services review in East Sussex. His work is concerned with various aspects of health economics, finance and management and he has published widely in this area.

Anna Dixon is Research Officer with the European Observatory on Health Care Systems and part-time Lecturer in European health policy at the London School of Economics. During her time at the Observatory she has organised and taught on summer schools for senior health policy makers from Eastern Europe and edited a series of country reports on the health care systems of Austria, Germany, Portugal, Switzerland and the UK. Her research interests mainly focus on health care reform trends, European health care systems and methods of funding health care. Recent publications include Funding health care: options for Europe published by the Open University Press and Health Care Systems in Eight Countries: Trends and Challenges prepared for HM Treasury.

## Acknowledgements

The Fabian Society would also like to thank Aventis for their generous support in funding this pamphlet. As always, it is recognised that their support for the project does not imply that this report reflects their views.

# Introduction

The NHS has been a political battlefield for the last ten years. The internal market reforms introduced by the Conservative Government in 1991 unleashed a programme of radical change that was hotly contested and debated throughout its lifetime. The incoming Labour Government of 1997, reacting especially to the excessive administration costs and inequity believed to be associated with the internal market, was pledged to replace it. But its own reforms, as set out in *The NHS Plan* and *Delivering the NHS Plan* have also been the subject of intense scrutiny. Alternative prescriptions from opposition parties and assorted think-tanks have proliferated.

This is the context in which the Fabian Society decided to launch a Health Policy Forum on the direction of health policy in the UK. The meetings of the Forum took place over the course of 2002 and brought together a diverse group of participants including ministers and other politicians, health professionals, representatives of user groups, academics, NHS and private sector managers (see appendix). This report draws on the presentations and discussions that took place at the Forum, but the central analysis and arguments are those of the authors and do not necessarily reflect the views of those who participated in the meetings.

1

In seeking to make some sense of the often tangled debate surrounding UK health policy it is helpful to distinguish between questions relating to the finance of health care and questions relating to its supply or delivery.

Much of the debate surrounding the NHS for the past 25 years has centred on its finance, or to be more precise, its inadequate funding. High profile media accounts of hospital bed shortages, patients waiting on trolleys in accident and emergency departments and long waiting times for non-urgent treatments have painted a picture of an underfunded service staggering from one crisis to the next. This state of affairs has given rise to numerous proposals for alternatives to a general tax-funded system on the grounds that this system seems incapable of producing sufficient levels of funding. That is levels that people indicate that they would like to see spent on the NHS in public opinion polls and other expressions of citizens views. We consider some of these proposals in Chapter 1, 'Raising the money'.

'Raising the money' shows that proposals for earmarked or hypothecated taxes, moves towards European style social health insurance schemes, and proposals for a greater role for private payments and private health insurance have all had their advocates. Earmarking taxes for spending on health care has been seen as a means of providing greater transparency, increasing taxpayers' willingness to pay and releasing the NHS budget from annual spending constraints. The apparently better-funded health systems in France, Germany and the Netherlands have led to claims that social health insurance is capable of delivering higher levels of funding than a general tax-based system. Others have argued that lower UK spending levels on health care are primarily the result of lower levels of supplementary private expenditure and that these need to be boosted.

Our own view is that the NHS spending plans for the period up to 2008 announced in the 2002 budget have defused the finance debate, at least in the short to medium term. Over this period real spending on the NHS is planned to grow from £65 billion to £105 billion: an unprecedented, sustained rate of real growth of 7.4 per cent per year. By 2008 it is expected that health spending in the UK will represent about 9.4 per cent of GDP, close to average spending in the EU. Of course, it may be that overall economic performance and the state of public finances do not allow the expenditure plans to be realised. There is always an element of risk and this has been heightened by the turbulence in world finance markets in recent months. History also tells us that, no matter what the level of funding, dissatisfaction with the inevitable limitations of the status quo will almost certainly result in continued proposals for new forms of health finance.

Notwithstanding these reservations, we believe that the main challenges facing UK health policy over the next few years lie not on the finance side, but on the delivery side. It is questions about how the extra funding is used to improve health services that need to be addressed over the short-to-medium term. In fact, the White Paper *Delivering the NHS Plan: next steps on investment, next steps on reform* sets out an agenda for addressing this task. We pick up some of the major components of this agenda in the remainder of this report.

Chapter 2, 'Investing wisely', considers exactly how increased levels of funding should be used to maximum effect. In doing so we start with the too often neglected role of public health and prevention. Most of the high profile public debate about the NHS centres on shortcomings in the acute hospital sector. Indeed focus group discussions held by the Labour Party prior to the 1997 election identified waiting times for hospital treatment as the number one priority. In this climate it is not surprising that most recent NHS reform has centred on acute care. But this perspective is narrow and short sighted. Many of the problems of the acute sector are the result of inadequate public health and preventative programmes. Emergency hospital admissions for strokes and falls among elderly people are just one example of a major pressure on the acute sector that could be reduced with greater attention to preventative programmes.

'Investing wisely' also considers the major new efforts being devoted to improving NHS services through the work of the National Institute for Clinical Excellence (NICE) and the production of National Service Frameworks (NSFs). NICE has been set up to examine evidence on the clinical and cost effectiveness of new health care technologies and to make recommendations as to whether they should be provided by the NHS. NSFs build on this evidence and set out national standards on the ways that services should be organised and the ways that patients should be treated. We believe that the general thrust of this approach is sound but that certain shortcomings in its methodology and implementation process need to be addressed if it is to realise its full potential.

NICE is a key component of the Government's approach to the perennial necessity to prioritise or ration limited NHS services. It provides the opportunity to base hard decisions on evidence of clinical and cost effectiveness. But it operates within an environment where the scope of the NHS remains ill-defined. In theory it provides comprehensive services, but in practice delay and denial are widespread. We believe that there is a strong case for following the example of a number of social insurance based countries in setting out more explicitly NHS entitlements that patients can expect. 'Investing wisely' discusses how this could be done.

The reliance that the Government is placing on national organisations such as NICE and The Commission for Healthcare Audit and Inspection raises questions about the appropriate balance between central direction and control (in the interests of NHS principles, national standards and accountability) and local decision making and autonomy (in the interests of local responsiveness, flexibility and innovation). This issue is dealt with in Chapter 3, 'National standards versus local autonomy'.

There are no easy answers to the dilemma of finding an acceptable balance between central control and the devolution of responsibility to local decision makers. The Government's current stance is to rely upon a strong system of central direction, where standards are set nationally and monitored through a top down system of performance management, but to offer greater freedom and devolution of decision-making powers to selected local organisations. This is referred to as the policy of earned autonomy. Through the application of this policy, selected NHS organisations, whether primary care trusts or hospitals, will be granted greater freedom from central direction as they prove their ability to perform to a high standard. In 'National standards versus local autonomy' we examine how this system is developing and can be expected to develop in the future. Our conclusion is that there is presently an excessive amount of central direction and that this imbalance needs to be addressed. We believe that the government needs to place more confidence in local decision makers rather than less and to steer with a lighter touch.

One of the main criticisms of the old-style NHS has been the limited choice offered to patients. Numerous commentators have compared the UK situation unfavourably with other European countries. The Government recognises many of these criticisms and in *Delivering the NHS Plan* has set out several proposals for enhancing patient choice. We support the Government's general aims in relation to choice but believe that more attention needs to be paid to the dimensions of choice that are to be enhanced and some of the trade-offs likely to be involved. These questions are dealt with in Chapter 4, 'Choices in health care'. We draw on international evidence to highlight dimensions of choice in relation to health insurers, first contact providers, hospitals and types of treatment. We also raise the thorny issue of the possible trade-off of greater choice for some people and the resultant increase in inequality of access. Careful thought needs to be given to striking the right balance between choice and access. Developments in this area need to be subjected to evaluation and equity audit.

One of the most surprising elements of the Government's current supply-side reform programme has been the enhanced role expected to be carried out by private sector providers. The traditional bete noire of successive Labour governments is now embraced as a source of greater plurality, diversity and choice. This major change of stance was cemented in a concordat between the Secretary of State and the Independent Healthcare Association signed in October 2000. This was based on the premise that there should be no organisational or ideological barriers to the delivery of high quality health services. The government takes the view that the boundary between public and private is both arbitrary and outmoded. What is important is what works.

Since the signing of the concordat there have been a whole raft of ministerial statements reinforcing the emphasis placed on the private provision of services for NHS funded patients. These are considered in Chapter 5 of the report, 'Plurality and the private sector'. We believe that as long as the equity aims of the NHS are preserved through the finance system, there is no compelling reason in principle against the development of a more pluralist health care delivery system. Consequently we believe that this is a worthwhile exploratory strategy. However, we also believe that there are many questions that remain unanswered in terms of relative cost effectiveness, uneven quality assurance mechanisms and a yet-to-be-tested regulatory regime. For this reason we think that much closer attention should be paid to the collection of evaluative, empirical evidence as part of the development of this policy.

Taken overall, we believe that there are many aspects of *The NHS Plan* and *Delivering the NHS Plan* that need much more refinement and development. But our key message is that a workable programme of supply-side reform has been set by the government for the next ten years. What is now needed is a period of stability in which to bring about sustainable service improvements with greater continuity than has been evident over the last decade.

# 1 | Raising the money

Levels of health spending in the UK have lagged behind comparable European countries for many years. In 1999, spending as a proportion of GDP amounted to 10.3 per cent in Germany, 9.3 per cent in France, 8.7 per cent in the Netherlands, but only 6.8% per cent in the UK (see graph below). The recent review carried out for the Treasury by Sir Derek Wanless and his team estimated a cumulative underspend of £267 billion (1998 prices) over the period 1972 to 1998 compared with the EU average spend. The consequences of tight funding for patients in terms of long waiting times for hospital appointments, cancelled operations and treatment in often poor quality hospital wards and buildings are all too familiar.

For many commentators, these low levels of funding and associated shortages of capacity are a direct result of the method of raising NHS revenue, namely, through central taxation. As long ago as 1965 the Nobel laureate economist James Buchanan wrote of the 'inconsistencies of the NHS', an inconsistency that results in individuals as patients consistently demanding more services than they are prepared to fund as voters and taxpayers. According to this view, the only way to escape from tight Treasury control of the purse strings is to find new ways of financing the health service. In the last year many of the familiar candidates have once again received attention. These include an earmarked or hypothecated health tax, social health insurance, increased user charges and private health insurance. What are the pros and cons of these alternatives?

**Total expenditure on health in the United Kingdom and selected countries as a percentage of gross domestic product (GDP) 1980-1999**

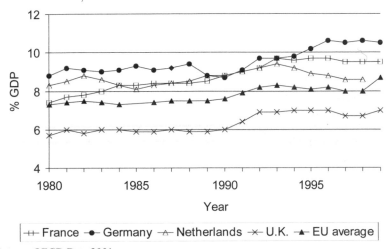

Source: OECD Data 2001

## An earmarked health tax

Earmarked (or hypothecated) taxes are not a new idea, but there has been a resurgence of interest in them recently. The British Medical Association has claimed that hypothecation offers a range of benefits. The idea also received support as part of the Fabian Commission on Taxation and Citizenship. The Secretary of State for Health has indicated his sympathy with earmarking, although the Liberal Democrats are the only mainstream party to declare their official support for the idea.

The main argument in favour of earmarking is that it would increase the transparency of the link between tax and spending and thus make people more willing to accept increases in taxation. Public opinion research conducted for the Fabian Commission showed that public willingness to pay increased taxes is higher if the extra money is for a specific area of public expenditure such as health or education. Another advantage is that it would free health spending decisions from political interference and the triennial spending reviews.

Despite traditional Treasury hostility to earmarking, the principle has already been conceded. In the 2000 budget, the additional revenue from the increase in tobacco duties was earmarked for the NHS. This is a form of soft earmarking. More comprehensive proposals would establish a stricter form of earmarking whereby most expenditure would be determined by revenue, i.e. a single tax stream would be identified for health. The only taxes which could generate sufficient revenues to cover current spending plans would be income tax or VAT or national insurance contributions.

However, there are a number of disadvantages associated with strict earmarking. First, there are questions about the extent to which hypothecation creates a real linkage between tax and spending? To have greater influence over levels of health spending, tax payers would need influence over tax rates. Spending would not become more responsive without some mechanism for 'preference revelation'. It is difficult to see how earmarking would offer this choice. More generally, Andrew Dilnot, when director of the Institute for Fiscal Studies, argued that hypothecation is: 'almost always a deceit... there is very rarely any real linkage between these sorts of taxes and the spending in the areas they purportedly go to'.

Second, spending levels would be more vulnerable to fluctuations in the economic cycle if they relied on one fixed revenue stream. There would be less scope for smoothing out spending year on year. Periods of economic recession could actually result in tighter constraints on health spending than apply at the moment. There are options for smoothing out such as the creation of an NHS Fund as proposed by the Fabian Commission on Taxation and Citizenship.

Third, hypothecation would reduce the flexibility of government to make trade-offs between health and other areas of public spending. This may well undermine efforts to promote 'joined-up policymaking'. This would be particularly undesirable in the case of public health policies, many of which are likely to fall outside the health budget e.g. housing, environment and transport.

Finally, it is difficult to see why health should constitute a special case for earmarking. If the approach has merit, why should it not be applied to all spending departments? The Treasury is surely right to be wary of the threat to its capacity for macro economic management carried in this particular Trojan horse. Overall, we believe that despite its superficial appeal, the case for hypothecation is a weak one. In particular, its supporters really need to be far clearer about the ways in which its alleged greater transparency will make aggregate health spending more responsive to citizens' diverse preferences.

## Social health insurance

Social health insurance (SHI) is similar to an earmarked payroll tax. Revenues are usually raised through compulsory contributions on wages and salaries from employers and employees. A distinctive feature of social health insurance schemes is that finances are usually managed by independent insurance funds, also called sickness funds. The fact that more generously funded health care systems in countries such as Germany, France and the Netherlands rely on social insurance has led to considerable interest in their possible adoption in the UK, particularly by think-tanks on the right of the political spectrum. The case for social insurance is usually based on three main assertions:

■ *Social health insurance systems spend more on health*

The argument, similar to that for an earmarked tax, is that people are more willing to pay higher social insurance contributions because they are more visible and they feel they get something in return for their payments (the notion of connectedness). It is certainly true that spending levels are higher in many SHI countries. But the picture is more complicated than it at first appears. The Eurobarometer survey collects data on the attitudes of EU citizens towards, amongst other things, health spending in different countries. Interestingly, it shows that support for increased spending on health is currently low in many SHI countries such as Germany and Austria, suggesting that contribution rates may have already reached a point above which people are reluctant to contribute increased amounts. In contrast, willingness to spend more in quite generously funded, tax-based systems is sometimes greater as in Sweden.

It would also be a mistake to assume that higher spending levels in the past were necessarily a reflection of user preferences. Many of these SHI countries have relied upon payment systems in which doctors and hospitals have simply submitted bills to sickness funds and been reimbursed. Higher levels of spending may well reflect supplier-induced demand and weak expenditure control.

■ *Social health insurance systems allow more choice*

Another attraction of SHI is that it offers more choice to insurees. In a number of countries individuals have the right to select a sickness fund, and to change funds if they are not satisfied. Both Germany and the Netherlands currently attach considerable importance to consumer choice and to competition between funds for insurees. But this aspect should not be overstated. Because benefit packages are usually standardised across sickness funds, the domain of choice is often restricted. Moreover, in some other countries, sickness funds still operate as monopolies because they are either employer or territorially based as in France and Austria. Choice of doctor or hospital is a common feature of many SHI systems, but it is not unique to them. For example, it is also offered in tax-based systems such as Sweden and Denmark.

Greater choice figures particularly highly in the case for SHI made by think tanks on the right. But for them it has additional attributes. They tend to favour a Swiss-style system with the compulsory purchase by individuals of community rated policies (i.e. premiums based upon average population risks rather than individual health risks) from private insurers, rather than a Bismarck model with employer/employee contributions to non-profit sickness funds. Moreover, they are attracted by the opt-out allowed in some SHI schemes, whereby individuals earning over a certain income may choose to purchase private insurance as a substitute for public insurance and be exempt from SHI contributions. Both of these features involve a greater role for private sector finance.

■   *Social health insurance systems are as fair as tax-based systems*

Advocates of SHI claim that it promotes social solidarity by offering near-to-universal coverage and by relating premiums to ability to pay, that is, income. As far as income is concerned, the historical roots of social health insurance as an income replacement for periods of ill health mean that contributions are levied

13

as a proportion of income. In Austria, Germany, Luxembourg and the Netherlands, however, there is an upper ceiling on contributions, and so the schemes are slightly regressive. In contrast, income tax is progressive; although the overall the progressivity of general taxation will depend on the mix of direct and indirect taxation. In terms of equity of access, tax funded systems are universal allowing everyone equal access (though there may be barriers to access in practice such as queues). Social health insurance systems have achieved near-to-universal coverage through the gradual extension of coverage to the self employed and non working groups. However, there are still (small) groups of the population who are not covered and rely on social services to provide them with care.

Looked at overall, it seems that SHI systems may have some marginal advantages over a central tax based system in terms of additional choice, but this needs to be set against a major disadvantage associated with their possible introduction in the UK. This is that the institutional structure of sickness funds simply does not exist in the UK. To create such a structure would incur heavy set up costs. In addition, the continuing costs of administering social health insurance (or transaction costs) would also be higher due to the multiplicity of collection agents and funds, and the complex risk adjustment mechanisms for redistributing resources between funds.

Finally, it should be recognised that just as some UK commentators are looking towards SHI countries, these countries are expressing concerns about the performance of their systems. The costs imposed on employment through SHI is a particularly serious concern, leading to industrialists' claims of reduced international competitiveness. Furthermore, earned income is growing more slowly than investment income in many countries. Retaining the ability to raise taxes from various sources, including investment income and company profits, makes it possible to adjust for this differential growth. Already most SHI systems have a significant tax component, either in the form of transfers to the sickness funds, subsidies for hospitals or paying off the deficits of the funds, and these components are growing.

## User charges

User charges represent only about 2 per cent of NHS income. The vast majority of NHS services are provided totally free at the point of use, although user charges have been applied increasingly in the case of pharmaceutical prescriptions, ophthalmic and dental services. No serious commentator has ever suggested that user charges should become a major source of NHS revenue. But calls for the extension of user charges in order to make patients more aware of the cost of health services, and to deter frivolous use, are voiced with striking regularity. Proposals for levying fees for GP consultations fall into this category.

User charges have strong appeal for those people who wish to encourage greater individual responsibility. Moreover, there is research evidence to support the claim that user charges do reduce health service usage across a range of services extending from pharmaceutical prescriptions to hospital admissions. Evidence from the United States, notably the RAND Health Insurance Experiment, and a growing body of European evidence is now available pointing to the quantitative impact of different levels of charging[1]. The problem is, however, that charges are a very blunt instrument. They tend to reduce the use of appropriate as well as inappropriate services. As such, they often have an adverse effect on health outcomes. Moreover, they tend to impact disproportionately on low income, deprived and vulnerable groups, such as elderly people and those with chronic illnesses. As Gordon Brown, the Chancellor of the Exchequer, has put it, user charges mean simply that 'the sick pay more for being sick'.

For all of these reasons we believe that it would be unwise to contemplate a major expansion of user charging, despite the fact that they are widespread in many European countries. They may have some role to play at the margins, particularly in relation to non-clinical, hotel services. However, where charges are applied in clinical areas, careful consideration needs to be given to the services to which they are applied, levels and types of charging and to exemptions.

## Private health insurance

Private health insurance has never been seriously proposed as a wholesale alternative to the NHS. The example of the US health care system where over 40 million people are without medical insurance at any one time is reason enough to reject this model as a major source of finance. Many of the uninsured are working people who simply cannot afford the premiums charged by private health insurance companies. Even middle income families are finding the cost of insurance difficult to cope with, especially as most insurance policies require large copayments to be made by the claimants. And the situation seems set to get worse according to a recent Commonwealth Fund report with two in five adults with employer-sponsored coverage reporting paying more for their premiums, higher co-payments, or receiving reduced benefits in 2001.[2] In short, private health insurance along US lines is associated with price inflation, inequitable access and poor expenditure control.

Private health insurance in Europe is more commonly a complement or supplement to some form of public cover. This is also true in the UK. Private health insurance cover may entitle people to be covered for services not fully covered by the NHS (for example, plans covering dental treatment) or, more importantly, may enable people to purchase additional qualitative features such as faster access to services or treatment by a consultant of their choice. Typically people with private insurance use both the NHS and the private sector. They do not opt out of the NHS but have 'double cover'. Private health insurance policies therefore do not need to be comprehensive. In fact they are highly selective.

The Conservative Party announced in 2002 that if elected they propose to introduce tax relief for those purchasing private health insurance, as occurs in Australia, as well as those paying for care directly. They claim that this would reduce the burden on the NHS. However, the economic case for offering tax incentives on premiums is questionable because large amounts of finance would be transferred to insurees who already have private insurance (amounting to a so called 'deadweight loss') as well as new insurees attracted by the tax concessions. Moreover, such a policy is likely to be regressive as the distribution of private health insurance is heavily skewed towards the higher socio-economic groups, those aged 45-64 and those in employment. So while a case for supplementary private insurance can be made on grounds of increased choice, the case for tax incentives is weak in terms of both efficiency and equity.

## Health finance reform - why now?

Debates about the respective merits of different methods of health finance have a long history. Nearly ten years ago the health economist, Tim Ensor, summarised the relative performance of general taxation, social insurance and private insurance in terms of key criteria of efficiency, equity, choice and transparency (see Table 1). Despite the renewed debate about funding in the UK, the same observations remain relevant today. In these terms, the UK tax-based system seems to perform rather well. It has managed to contain the growth in aggregate health spending more effectively than most other systems and has thereby minimised the overall burden on the economy. At the micro

**The performance of alternative health financing systems**

| Criteria | General taxation | Social insurance | Private insurance |
|---|---|---|---|
| **Macro efficiency** | Global, cash limited budgets. Strong cost control | Demand-led systems offer poor cost control<br><br>Global budgets strengthen cost control<br><br>Transparency of payments increases user/payer cost consciousness | Demand-led and absence of global budgets. Poor cost control |
| **Micro efficiency** | Low administrative costs<br><br>Work incentives depend upon forms of taxation | Multiple insurers/ sickness funds increase administrative costs<br><br>A tax on employment | Multiple insurers lead to high transactions and administrative costs<br><br>Employment based insurance represents a 'tax' on employment |
| **Equity** | Universal coverage<br><br>Payments related to ability to pay as defined by the tax system | Near to universal coverage<br><br>Payments related to ability to pay Can be more or less progressive than a tax based system depending on the precise structure of tax and SHI payment | Major gaps in coverage<br><br>Contributions based upon risk ratings rather than ability to pay |
| **Choice** | No choice over contribution rates or between insurers | Little choice over rates of contribution but generally some choice between insurers | Considerable choice over insurance premiums (and associated benefits packages) and between insurers* |
| **Transparency** | Weak link between tax payments and spending on health care | An earmarked tax providing a general link between payments and spending on health care | A close link between individual payments and individual health benefits |

*Less so where employment-based insurance.

level, it avoids the excessive administrative costs and the potentially damaging consequences of an employment tax, found to different degrees in both private and social insurance systems. It also seems to be rather more equitable in the way that it raises finance.

Set against these advantages, there has been the perennial complaint that aggregate cost control has been too tight. Service levels have simply not kept pace with other European countries. To the extent that there has been a case for examining alternative sources of finance, underfunding has been the reason. But the Chancellor's 2002 budget has surely laid this case to rest - at least in the medium term. Over the 5 year period from 2003/4 to 2007/8, the NHS is due to receive real terms increases in expenditure of 7.4 per cent per year. This will increase the budget over this period from £65 billion to £105 billion (after allowing for inflation) and represent a rise in the share of GDP devoted to health from 7.7 per cent to 9.4 per cent. Some idea of the size of these increases can be gauged from the fact that over the period 1954-2000 annual increases in real expenditure averaged 3.7 per cent. Current plans will double this rate.

In view of these commitments, we believe that proposals for alternative methods of finance are currently an irrelevance. Underfunding no longer seems endemic to a central tax-based system. Of course, economic circumstances may change and the admittedly ambitious plans may be thrown into doubt. In these circumstances, alternative sources of funding may once again emerge as important policy issues. But for the time being we believe that the major challenges facing UK health policy lie not on the finance side but the delivery or supply side. It is to these challenges that we now turn.

# 2 | Investing wisely

The NHS is set to receive unprecedented increases in funding over the next five years. This is certainly very good news. But there are dangers. Making effective use of such large increases in funding in the short term will not be easy. Service plans based upon the increased funding levels envisage an increase of 15,000 consultants and GPs, an extra 35,000 nurses, midwives and health visitors; and 42 new hospitals by 2008. Clearly these cannot be made available overnight. In the short term there is bound to be a shortage of capacity. Major cash injections in the face of limited inputs may simply serve to drive up prices rather than produce extra services.

In fact this is already happening. In many areas, private sector beds are being purchased by the NHS in an effort to boost short-term capacity. But as utilisation levels rise, so do private sector prices. There is evidence of rises in both consultants' private fees and private hospital charges.

Within the NHS, the nursing workforce is well aware that 'Milburn's millions' are available and their pay demands are being framed accordingly. In fact, given nursing shortages and low levels of morale associated with NHS pay and conditions, there is a strong case for nursing pay increases. But this is an issue that is best addressed through an overall reform of nursing pay and conditions - in the light of recruitment and retention difficulties - not through opportunistic wage demands.

In the face of these dangers, the overriding challenge for the Department of Health, and more specifically the NHS, is to spend and invest the Chancellor's largesse wisely - and be seen to do so. The stakes are high both for the government but also personally for the Chancellor. The Treasury and Parliament will be monitoring closely the returns on their investment. Future funding increases will no doubt depend on these returns being delivered.

The main instrument of accountability being used by the Treasury for this purpose is the Public Service Agreement (PSA). This makes explicit the aim of the Department of Health for 2003-2006: 'Transform the health and social care system so that it produces faster, fairer services that deliver better health and tackle health inequalities.' This broad aim is specified in terms of three main objectives: to improve service standards, to improve health and social care outcomes for everyone and to improve value for money. In the PSA new targets are set and old ones renewed. These include:

- maximum waiting times of 3 months for outpatient appointments and 6 months for inpatient treatment by 2005
- booked appointments for all hospital appointments by 2005
- reductions in waiting times for accident and emergency treatment
- access to a primary care doctor within 48 hours from 2004

The health targets include:

- reductions in health inequalities, mortality rates from cancer and heart disease, and suicide rates amongst those with mental health problems

21

- increase the number of drug users in drug treatment programmes, elderly people receiving intensive home care support and educational attainment of children in care

Value for money targets require a reduction in unit costs, and improvements in quality, to contribute to an improvement in cost efficiency of at least 2 per cent a year.

Parliament will hold the NHS accountable through an annual report to be published by the new Commission for Healthcare Audit and Inspection (CHAI). This will bring together the work of the Audit Commission on value for money in health, the work of the Commission for Health Improvement and the role of the National Care Standards Commission in inspecting private health care providers.

We consider this accountability framework and its likely impact later in this report. But at this point we want to emphasise two important aspects of the agenda faced by the Department of Health in the task of spending wisely. These are, first, the need to re-emphasise health as opposed to health care and, second, the need to recognise the limits of the NHS and to allocate limited budgets in a clinically and cost effective manner.

## Spending on health or health care?

It is well known that the health of the population depends on a diverse range of factors, most of them outside the health care sector itself. Housing and the environment, nutrition, lifestyle and welfare policies all exert major influences on health. The 1998 report from Sir Donald Acheson, Independent inquiry into inequalities in health, highlighted once again the importance of policies outside health in improving population health and reducing health inequalities.

During the first term of the present government the aim of reducing health inequalities became a key policy objective. The launching of initiatives such as Health Action Zones in areas of particular deprivation signalled a multi-agency approach to the problem. The creation of a ministerial post for Public Health highlighted the importance attached to the wider health perspective, and a commitment to 'joined up' government seemed to signal an inter-departmental approach to the task. It seemed that the wider determinants of ill health were being taken seriously and that there was a recognition that health is not synonymous with health care.

However since that time the commitment to a wider public health strategy seems to have slipped down the government's agenda. It is now health care and not health that seems to be a key preoccupation not only of the Secretary of State for Health but the Government in general. Public health is now the remit of a parliamentary under secretary reflecting its diminished authority and prominence.

This shift of emphasis has been partly driven by public opinion, abetted by the media, which has repeatedly highlighted the failings of the NHS. Public health rarely produces short term gains and is less dramatic in impact than many heroic acute service treatments. The political imperative to see improvements in the standard of services within the NHS has meant that health care dominates the national policy agenda. Organisational changes have also contributed to this trend. The separation of powers between the NHS Executive and the Department of Health provided some division of functions in which the public health agenda could develop. But this division has now been partly reversed. The post of Permanent Secretary and Chief Executive of the NHS is now combined. Moreover, in practice, the Secretary of State for Health has a wide range of executive powers over the NHS. As such the NHS rather than health dominates his agenda.

Within the NHS, at the micro level, other organisational

changes are also threatening the public health function. The decision to abolish health authorities and devolve many of their functions to primary care trusts has caused a major disruption in departments of public health previously located at health authority level. These departments have been split up with public health specialists being allocated to individual primary care trusts. This carries a very real danger of professional isolation and an absence of the critical mass necessary to carry out their functions effectively.

Neglect of the public health agenda and the wider determinants of health can have major expenditure implications. This is demonstrated quite vividly by the work of the Wanless review. The review team estimated NHS spending up to 2022/3 in terms of three scenarios: 'solid progress' (i.e. steady improvements with the current public health targets being met and maintained), 'slow uptake' (i.e. levels of health inequalities and risk factors remain unchanged) and 'fully engaged' (i.e. rapid improvements in health underpinned by a high quality service). These alternative scenarios produced spending projections ranging from £154 billion to £184 billion. One of the key factors underlying the different scenarios was the health of the population. Under the fully engaged scenario, not only would people be living longer but they would spend a smaller proportion of their lives in ill health. This assumed dramatic improvements in public health with sharp declines in smoking and obesity resulting in reduced utilisation of health services. Calculations such as these make very clear the relationship between increased spending on public health and health promotion and reduced longer-term spending on health care.

We believe that the reduced emphasis that currently seems to be placed upon public health and the wider determinants of health represents a major gap in the Government's thinking. This is particularly serious shortcoming given the need to invest new monies in health. The essence of investment is to spend in the present in order to reap returns in the future. If the health of the population is actively improved through the use of cost effective public health interventions, less will need to be spent on health care in the longer term.

## What to spend the money on in the NHS?

Even with increased funding on the scale projected over the next five years, the NHS will still need to set priorities about which clinical services to fund. Achieving the best results will mean targeting resources on clinically and cost effective treatments. In an environment where resources will always be limited in relation to needs, decisions will need to be made about how best to allocate resources, to which patients and for what treatments. This is the vexed area of rationing or priority setting.

For most of its history rationing decisions in the NHS were made on an ad hoc local basis, often disguised as clinical decisions. A major impetus for greater transparency and openness in the priority setting process was the establishment of health authorities as purchasers of services as part of the internal market reforms of 1991. For the first time, organisations with a collective responsibility for a resident population started to consider explicitly what services should be provided within limited budgets. Both financial and clinical factors came into play as health authorities issued guidance about what was and was not to be made available under the NHS. This process did not always proceed smoothly. Some high profile court cases followed, usually involving the denial of services. The term 'post code' prescribing entered the NHS lexicon as treatments were available on the NHS in some areas but not in others.

With the devolution of budgets and commissioning to primary care trusts (PCTs), these rationing decisions will affect smaller population groups and will impinge on primary as well as secondary care services. PCTs will be crucial in deciding what to spend money on and shaping the services on offer to patients. This is bound to create some tensions that have yet to be resolved. In particular, there is likely to be a tension between PCTs being responsive to local needs and the unacceptability of variation in service provision between local areas.

The Governments current response to this tension is to 'encourage local responsiveness but within a strong national framework. Two key components of this national framework are the National Institue for Clincal Excellence (NICE) and National Service Frameworks (NSFs). NICE was established in 1999 and is tasked with producing and disseminating evidence-based information on the clinical and cost effectiveness of existing and new health care technologies. It operates by issuing recommendations to the Secretary of State on whether technologies should be financed by the NHS for all of the population or for particular groups in the population, or whether further clinical trials are needed. In addition NICE produces guidelines on the management of specific conditions and undertakes clinical audit.

To complement the clinical guidelines produced by NICE, national service frameworks (NSFs) set out national standards on how services should be organised and the ways that patients should be treated. Already NSFs have been produced for cancer, paediatric intensive care, mental health, coronary heart disease, older people and diabetes. Further NSFs on renal services, children services and long term neurological conditions are in the pipeline. Whilst NICE guidance is based on technical reports commissioned to academic experts, NSFs are compiled by civil servants on the basis of advice from an external reference group. The group is composed of representatives of health professionals, service users, carers, health service managers and partner agencies such as social services.

We believe that NICE and NSFs represent a commendable

attempt to move health care provision onto a more rational, evidence-based footing. However, there are still a number of technical difficulties associated with their approaches, as well as some broader political/cultural problems associated with their implementation.

As far as technical difficulties are concerned, it is clearly impossible for NICE to examine all existing and new technologies. Its limited budget has meant that it has tended to focus on new technologies, predominantly new pharmaceutical drugs. This partial focus carries the danger that it may recommend marginally cost effective new treatments - which thereby receive priority for funding - whilst diverting funding away from more cost effective existing services, such as hip replacements and cataract surgery. This problem is bound to become larger as NICE recommendations become mandatory on PCTs. If extra funding is not made available to fund NICE recommendations, money will have to be found by shifting resources away from other services. Unless comparative information about the relative cost effectiveness of these displaced technologies is available, the NHS may allocate resources less efficiently than before.

It has been clear for some time that the evidence-based policy advocates have a rather naive view about the way in which research evidence is translated into practice. In its early phase NICE has devoted most of its resources to the science of assembling and evaluating evidence, and making recommendations. The fact that some of its judgements have attracted fierce opposition from user and pressure groups, e.g. the use of beta interferon for multiple sclerosis (MS) sufferers, seemed to be something that it had not anticipated, or at least had underestimated. It is now in the process of setting up citizens' panels to widen its perspective. Similar efforts will need to be made in terms of convincing local practitioners of the merits of NICE recommendations if they are to be absorbed into clinical practice.

One approach that may contribute to this process - by raising the profile of what can and cannot be provided by the NHS - would be a move towards establishing user entitlements in relation to NHS services.

## Entitlements to health care

In theory the NHS is a comprehensive service. The National Health Service Act 1977 requires the Secretary of State to promote a comprehensive health service designed to secure improvement in the physical and mental health of the population and to develop services for the prevention, diagnosis and treatment of illness. At a general level, the 1977 Act imposes a number of responsibilities on the Secretary of State in relation to the provision of hospital and community health services. However, for the most part, there is a large degree of discretion about the range of services that are actually provided. Thus the Secretary of State is required to provide services 'to such extent as he considers necessary to meet all reasonable requirements'.

The current open-ended arrangement leaves the NHS open to new and unconstrained demands. To quote the BMA Funding Review: "The concept of the NHS as a comprehensive service may have outlived its usefulness".

So what is the alternative ? In many social health insurance systems, benefits are specified. For example in Germany the Social Code Book V (1998, which governs the operation of social health insurance, contains a broad statement of entitlements. It states that insured persons are entitled to services for the protection against illness, early identification of disease and the treatment of disease. Insured persons are entitled to medical and complementary rehabilitation services, which are necessary to prevent a serious disability or need for care.

These entitlements are elaborated in further articles. For example, the scope of treatment of disease is defined as:

28

- Medical treatment including psychotherapy as a medical and psychotherapeutic treatment.
- Dental care including false teeth
- Treatment with pharmaceuticals, dressings and remedies
- Home nursing care and domestic help
- Hospital care
- Medical and complementary therapies for rehabilitation, capacity tests and occupational therapy.

Finally, a separate catalogue of reimbursable services specifies each intervention and the value assigned for reimbursement. This list is regularly updated with new medical procedures being added by the Federal Committee of Sickness Fund Physicians and Sickness Funds. More difficult is the task of removing old technologies or those which have been shown to have low effectiveness or poor cost effectiveness. The citizens' rights to receive these services can be challenged and or upheld by the social courts which are dedicated to matters relating to social insurance.

The general and discretionary statement that currently underpins the NHS could in the first instance be replaced by a broad but positive statement of the range of services to which all legal residents of the UK are entitled. This would also ensure greater parity between the constituent countries of the UK as devolution continues to create diversity in the organization of health care services. Finally it would make more explicit the connection between citizens, the taxes they pay and the benefits they receive.

A further step would be to define more positively the care which patients can expect from the NHS. As more national service frameworks are produced for different aspects of care these will establish a positive statement of the care to which patients are entitled under the NHS. These should be written with patients in mind and more efforts should be made to disseminate and promote them to patients. As with NICE decisions, there should be a statutory responsibility on Trusts to meet NSF standards.

Finally, an explicit package of benefits which are covered by the NHS could be produced. In effect there is already a list of pharmaceuticals in the form of the British National Formulary which indicates which of the approved drugs are not available on NHS prescription, though few patients are aware of how to access such information. Similarly NICE could establish a positive list of services funded by the NHS. Such a task may seem daunting and complex if it was to be established on a solely scientific basis (e.g. evidence of clinical and/or cost effectiveness). However, a first step would be to specify the range of services to which patients already have access under the NHS. This would provide a baseline against which future decisions of NICE could be placed. It must be clear that the decision as to whether treatment is justified in a particular case would remain a clinical decision.

There is of course the possibility that the establishment of entitlements to health care might increase litigation. Patients (or patient groups) might challenge the decisions of primary care trusts to withdraw funding from services included in the benefits package. Furthermore, legal challenges could be mounted against the government or an independent body charged with the task of defining entitlements over the exclusion of a treatment. Thus decisions about benefits could move from the consulting room to the courts resulting in massive legal costs. Litigation of this sort would not be new. There have been cases where patients have taken the health authority to court to rule on their right to receive a particular treatment. However, low cost procedures for the easy resolution of disputes could also be established to circumvent the need for lengthy (and costly) litigation. These might be similar, for example, to the appeals process in relation to NICE decisions.

It is likely that in the near future, decisions of the European Court of Justice are going to supercede national rulings anyway. Already two cases have challenged the right to determine what and when a patient receives treatment. Firstly, if a treatment is available in another EU member state which is 'usual in the professional circles concerned' then the home country is obliged to fund this treatment. Secondly, patients are allowed to seek care in another country if they are subject to an 'undue delay', again with the home country obliged to foot the bill. Ultimately free movement of patients may challenge the principle of subsidiarity (that is the right of Member States to determine how they run health care) and in due course lead to a EU-wide definition of a package of benefits.

## Spending wisely

*The NHS Plan* and *Delivering the NHS Plan* have set out an ambitious agenda for revitalising the NHS. It is vital that the substantial increases in funding provided through the Treasury are used to generate the improvements set out in the plan. Failure to achieve demonstrable improvements would undoubtedly unleash major attacks on the sustainability of the NHS. Yet we remain confident that *Delivering the NHS Plan* does set out a workable framework for achieving its aims. But it has gaps. Most notably, in our opinion, there is an almost total neglect of the role of public health. Spending wisely must mean reassessing the balance of both political and spending priorities between public health and health care. Beyond this, priority setting within the NHS will continue to require resources to be targeted on those services that are both clinically and cost effective. PCTs will assume challenging new roles in this process. NICE and NSFs provide innovative and promising approaches to these tasks, but are still in their infancy in terms of the crucial function of implementation. Finally, a shift towards a system based on entitle-ments would make a major contribution to not only ensuring that money was invested wisely but also establishing a stronger connection between taxes paid and benefits received.

In the next chapter, we move on to discuss how striking the right balance between national standard setting and local autonomy will be an important prerequisite for making the best use of the extra resources made available to the NHS through improved performance.

‘‘

# 3| National standards versus local autonomy

The discussion in 'Investing wisely' has shown how the Department of Health has set up a series of national organisations and mechanisms to establish, monitor and deliver national standards within the NHS. These include the National Institute for Clinical Excellence, National Service Frameworks and the Commission for Healthcare Audit and Inspection. The aim is to spread best practice throughout the NHS and to thereby reduce variations in service quality. At the same time, however, a major programme involving devolved decision making is being launched through the creation of primary care trusts (PCTs) and foundation hospitals. PCTs will control 75 per cent of the NHS budget and will be responsible for providing primary and community health services and commissioning secondary care services. Proposals for foundation hospitals envisage them enjoying far greater freedom and autonomy over, inter alia, capital expenditure and the pay and conditions of their workforce. The twin tenets of local autonomy are greater responsiveness to local needs and freedom for managers to operate in flexible and innovative ways.

But how exactly will the tension between central regulation and local freedom be resolved? The Government's answer is through earned autonomy. Through the application of this policy, selected NHS organisations, whether PCTs or hospital trusts, will be granted greater freedom from central regulation as they demonstrate their ability to perform to a high standard. But this an untried policy. How is the balance between local autonomy and central regulation likely to pan out in practice? Early indications from PCT development, proposals for foundation hospitals and policy on national standard setting are not, in our view totally reassuring.

## A primary care led NHS?

One aspect of GP fundholding that is widely held to have been successful, devolution of decision making to primary care organisations through budgetary responsibility, has become the cornerstone on which primary care trusts have been built. In common with GP fundholders, PCTs are responsible for both providing primary care services and commissioning secondary care on behalf of their registered populations. Unlike fundholding, GP membership of a PCT is compulsory and they are generally far larger organisations with more functions and considerably more complex governance structures.

PCTs have been developed at breakneck speed. The first seventeen were set up in April 2000 following the establishment of 481 primary care groups (PCGs) with more limited responsibilities a year earlier. Three subsequent waves followed in October 2000 (an additional 23 PCTs were set up), April 2001 (124 PCTs) and April 2002 (138 PCTs). By 1 April 2002 there were 302 PCTs in total (replacing the 481 PCGs), covering average populations of 170 000 people and controlling about 50 per cent of the NHS budget. By 2004, it is intended that they should control approximately 75 per cent of the NHS budget. This will be allocated directly from the Department of Health.

Thus, in a very short time, PCTs have assumed major responsibilities for developing primary and community health services and for commissioning secondary care services. Over the next two years they will take on even more functions. Simultaneous reorganisation on 1 April 2002 meant that the erstwhile health authorities were abolished and replaced by 28 strategic health authorities (SHAs). These SHAs have monitoring and performance management functions but no major commissioning responsibilities.

The emphasis on devolved responsibility to PCTs represents a continuation of a trend towards what was called, in the mid 1990s, a 'primary care led NHS'. It embodies a belief that decision making should be brought as close to the patient as possible. GPs and other primary care professionals are seen as being in the best position to respond to patients' needs. Moreover, better co-ordination with social care services, sometimes through the creation of special Care Trusts, is seen as an important element of the new arrangements. The combination of clinical and financial decision making, achieved through budget holding, is also seen as an important instrument for making more cost effective use of scarce resources.

The experience of fundholding showed that when GPs were given control of their budgets, they made better use of their resources; for example, there were large reductions in both unnecessary pharmaceutical prescriptions and patient referrals to hospitals. Newly available analysis of national data on GP fundholding shows that over the years that it was in operation, hospital referrals by fundholders were five per cent lower than by non-fundholders but that this differential disappeared with the abolition of fundholding.[3] Moreover, many innovations took place in primary care provision including the development of new services such as primary care-based counselling and consultant out reach clinics. Communication between hospital consultants and GPs also improved. According to one commentator, prior to GP fundholding, GPs sent Christmas cards to

35

consultants but during fundholding this trend was reversed!

Despite this favourable evidence and the potential gains from the development of primary care-based organisations such as PCTs, Ministers and the Department of Health are clearly nervous about their ability to take on major new responsibilities. They are an untried form of network organisation with complex management structures. Their scale and complexity means that earlier forms of primary care based purchasing organisations offer only limited lessons about how to undertake their commissioning and wider functions. Few PCTs have developed an effective commissioning role yet. Their limited management capacity is particularly apparent in areas such as finance where there are serious skills shortages at the senior level. Their complex governance structure involving both a board with non-executive members and an executive committee comprising professional members poses many problems concerning respective roles and responsibilities.

None of this should really be surprising. Creating so many new organisations in such a short space of time and expecting them to take on a large number of new and extended roles is extremely ambitious, to say the least. Recognition of the size of the task has led the Department of Health to set up a national development and support unit. But it has also strengthened the tendency to retain strong central control over a number of aspects of PCT activity. Will this simply apply during their early developmental stage? We doubt this. We are concerned that PCTs will not actually be given the freedom to realise their potential as primary care led organisations. Already they are being required to meet over 300 performance targets set by the centre. The danger is that they will become large, bureaucratic organisations in a command and control, line management structure - in short, reborn health authorities.

## Foundation hospitals

The counterpart to the policy of PCT devolved decision making in secondary care is the proposal for the creation of foundation hospitals. Unlike PCTs, NHS hospital trusts have a track record of managing their own affairs within a national framework since 1991 onwards. Moreover, they are not being offered major new freedoms across-the-board. Rather, selected organisations will be able to apply for foundation status.

At the present time, it is difficult to be precise about the form that foundation trusts will take. The first ones are not due to be set up in shadow form until July 2003 and will not become fully operational until after the appropriate legislation is passed in April 2004. Notwithstanding this uncertainty, official statements indicate that hospitals that are currently performing at the highest standard in terms of the NHS performance ratings, that is three star trusts, will be able to apply for foundation status. If successful, they will be offered greater freedom and independence to manage their affairs, although still remaining firmly within the NHS. Specifically these additional freedoms will include retention of revenues from land sales, freedom to determine their own investment plans and raise capital funds and the scope to offer additional performance-related rewards to staff. By placing foundation trusts outside direct line management and control from Whitehall, ministers expect to stimulate a wave of local entrepreneurship and innovation. New governance arrangements will ensure that they are locally owned organisations, that they pursue public sector values, but that they operate in a business like way.

Set against these expected advantages, critics have pointed out that the establishment of elite hospitals within the NHS carries dangers. It has been claimed that their freedom to set their own rates of pay will lead to less well paid staff being bid away from non-foundation, neighbouring hospitals. Given staff shortages in areas such as nursing, this would clearly have a detrimental effect on those hospitals losing staff. The spectre of hard pressed inner city hospitals serving deprived populations losing out to hospitals in leafy suburbs raises concerns about efficiency gains for some hospitals being achieved at the cost of more inequality in service standards overall.

Despite the apparent novelty of this approach even people with only a limited memory will recognise that we have been here before. The proposals for foundation hospitals are strikingly similar to the proposals for NHS trusts originally introduced through the Thatcher government's internal market reforms in 1991. Devolution of decision making to the local level alongside new freedoms over pay and conditions and capital spending were important elements of those reforms too. The subsequent history of that period with its failure to deliver the freedoms promised for NHS trusts offers some clear lessons for the foundation hospital proposals. Most notably that the requirements of public accountability meant that the Department of Health imposed an increasingly restrictive regulatory structure.

Echoes of these concerns are already being voiced in relation to foundation hospitals. Apart from the well known problems associated with the closure of failing hospitals - when access to services for local people is an important requirement - financial failure would bring a new set of problems. As a form of not-for-profit, public interest company, the Treasury would ultimately be responsible for its debt in the event of insolvency. Fears of hospital spending sprees for which the Treasury would ultimately be responsible but over which it would have little control are understandably making it lukewarm about the idea. While a rigorous selection process for foundation status may minimise the prospects of failure, the current performance management ratings to be used in this connection are imperfect and subject to large year-on-year changes. It is far more likely that each set of emerging problems associated with greater autonomy will be dealt with through tighter regulation.

## National standard setting

Within the framework of national standards, the newly established Commission for Healthcare Audit and Inspection (CHAI) will play a central role in the drive to monitor and improve standards. It will publish reports on the performance of NHS organisations, both individually and collectively, and will produce annual star ratings for all NHS organisations. In the case of persistent problems, CHAI will have the power to recommend special measures. These could include failing management being replaced by outside teams on a franchising basis.

An early indication of the workings of these star ratings is provided by the NHS Performance Ratings for Acute Trusts, Specialist Trusts and Mental Health Trusts 2001/02 published in July 2002. Acute trusts, for example, are assessed on a range of 'key targets' covering waiting times, cancelled operations, hospital cleanliness and their financial positions. Additional indicators relating to clinical performance (such as deaths within 30 days of surgery), readmissions, patient-focused measures (including patient surveys) and capacity and capability (e.g. data quality, staff opinions) are also taken into account. 36 trusts were allocated three star status, 77 received two star status, 35 received one star status and eight trusts received a zero star rating.

It is the Government's intention that the star rating system will prove a spur to improved performance over time, involving both carrots and sticks. Carrots will come in the form of increased autonomy, access to new funding and recognition of management achievements, whereas sticks will involve close monitoring and, ultimately, the replacement of failing management. How can this system be expected to operate? Looking back may provide some guide to the future.

## A little history

As the preceding discussion makes clear, the local autonomy proposed for PCTs and foundation hospitals has clear parallels with the greater autonomy proposed for NHS organisations during the period of the internal market. What does this earlier experience reveal about the pitfalls that will need to be avoided if a better balance between central direction and local autonomy is to be achieved this time than was achieved in the past?

To start with it has to be recognised that for most of its history, the NHS has operated with an essentially centrally-driven command and control structure. The existence of a national health service and the accountability of the Secretary of State for Health to Parliament has meant that successive ministers have sought to control the way that the service operates. Aneurin Bevan's much quoted claim that the noise from every dropped bed pan should reverberate in the Palace of Westminster is a graphic illustration of a long-standing ministerial mindset. Over a period of more than forty years NHS organisational structures were geared to this line management approach with administrative lines of authority from the Department of Health through, variously, regional health authorities, area health authorities, district health authorities and hospital units.

This history means that command and control is a deep seated feature of the NHS. The introduction of the internal market in 1991 might have been thought to constitute a break with this tradition. The contrast between the internal market and the previous command and control system hinged on the allocation of budgets to purchasers and devolved decision making to both purchasers and providers. Markets rely upon decentralised decisions and accountability is primarily downwards to consumers rather than upwards. The role of the centre is to set the rules and let the market participants get on with it. However, this laissez faire approach was always bound to pose problems in a national health service that remained politically accountable, and so it proved.

From the outset, when it was decreed that 'steady state' should apply in the early years, political considerations meant that the internal market was subjected to close central regulation and management. The early radicalism of Kenneth Clarke, as Secretary of State, gave way to a more cautious approach from his successors. Nowhere was this more vividly demonstrated than in London. Devolution of purchasing budgets to health authorities gave them freedom to decide where the money should be spent. Many health authorities outside London started to question why their patients were being referred to higher-cost London hospitals. Many started diverting patients to their local hospitals. The resultant reductions in demand for the services of the major inner London hospitals posed them with serious financial problems. Following the recommendations of the Tomlinson Inquiry, a major reconfiguration of London health services was called for. But the Government's response was to proceed cautiously and to moderate many of the purchaser-led effects of the internal market.

By 1997, the pressures associated with the introduction of an internal market to the NHS meant that regulation and market management were widespread. Some of this was for economic reasons - such as the need to pursue anti-monopoly policies - but much of it was because the political consequences of devolution were too great for ministers to ignore.

Clive Smee, then Chief Economic Adviser to the Department of Health, explained the situation in the following terms: 'Ministers and the centre are finding it difficult to reconcile devolved accountability with the demand for detailed monitoring created by parliamentary interest in operational issues. In consequence, the centre is drawn into a whole range of issues, from hospital catering standards to freedom of speech of hospital staff, that it once expected to leave to the discretion of local management. The dilemma is that without substantial operating freedom, trust management cannot be expected to produce better perform- ance... but that with such freedom there is bound to be diversity of behaviours and performance. The existence of outliers is then seen - by press, auditors and politicians - as a cause for central regulation.'

This is the crux of the problem. Those who believe that there is a case for greater devolution of decision making and freedom from central control are inevitably confronted with an NHS constrained by political considerations and a legacy of centralised command and control that has proved stubbornly resistant to change. A strong belief in devolution asserted itself with the introduction of the internal market, but was soon reined in. So what is the way forward for those who continue to believe in the merits of local autonomy?

## Steering with a light touch

Central government obviously has a major role to play in relation to the NHS. The service is publicly funded and the Secretary of State is accountable for it to Parliament. The desire to regulate the NHS centrally on the grounds of improved efficiency (e.g. reducing unacceptable cost and clinical variations) and equity (e.g. eliminating postcode prescribing) is laudable and an under- standable aim within a national health service. But we believe that this needs to be achieved through steering and not rowing. It is a role that the World Health Organisation has described as stewardship. It involves defining the vision and setting policy direction, but avoiding excessive intervention. Clearly there will be difficult trade-offs. Devolution of decision making will inevitably lead to diversity and variation. Why else encourage devolution? Within acceptable limits, this is a price that has to be paid for innovation and progress.

Equally important is the need to avoid excessive top-down performance monitoring and management. Apart from the potentially deleterious effect of excessive performance management on staff morale, there are the well known unintended consequences of management by performance indicators. These include tunnel vision (i.e. concentration on those areas covered by performance management to the exclusion of other important areas); myopia (i.e. concentration on short term gains rather than long term improvements); misrepresentation (i.e. the deliberate manipulation of data, including creative accounting); and gaming (i.e. altering behaviour in ways that are inconsistent with the regulators aim in order to obtain a strategic advantage).

Regulators have a history of failing to let go. Local innovation and enthusiasm is stifled as local organisations put excessive effort into managing upwards, otherwise known as feeding the beast, rather than managing downwards. Genuine service change is forfeited in the quest to meet national targets. Obsession with waiting times targets is a good example of a national standard that has undoubtedly diverted attention from more important clinical areas.

We believe that the Government needs to place more confidence in local decision makers rather than less. The decision to establish the Commission for Health Improvement and Audit as a 'a tough independent healthcare regulator/inspectorate' represents an unfortunate departure from the more developmental role that was gradually emerging from its predecessor's work. Punitive inspection is unlikely to generate a climate of trust, learning and improved performance. Mistrust and suspicion are not ingredients for improved performance. In short, the government needs to curb its interventionist tendencies and steer with a lighter touch.

One consequence of greater local autonomy will be more responsiveness to local users. The Government is anxious to

43

promote this responsiveness by offering more choice. We now turn to this aspect of the reform agenda.

# 4| Choices in health care

Patient choice has not traditionally been assigned much importance in the NHS. The Government believes that this attitude is out of date. The growth of consumerism in other areas of social and economic life means that the NHS must change. For this reason The NHS Plan and Delivering the NHS Plan set out an ambitious agenda for strengthening patient choice. Plans include more choice over hospitals for treatment and over the date and time of treatment. Initially these choices will be offered to patients who have been waiting more than six months for heart operations, but by 2005 it is expected that all patients will be able to book appointments both at the time and place of their choice. This approach will be underpinned by a greater availability of information so that choices can take place on an informed basis.

Few people would argue that offering greater choice in the NHS is not a good thing. But discussions of the subject often use the term 'choice' indiscriminately to refer to a whole range of policies each with particular implications for the patient and the health service. Given that other countries have a longer tradition of providing patients choice in health care, there is a strong case for examining the ways in which choice is offered around the world. This will provide a basis for answering two key questions:

how best can choice be extended in the NHS and what will be the impact on patients and the service?

# What choices?

Choice can operate on different levels. To unpick this complexity the table below indicates three different levels of choice and the forms of choice that operate at each level. First, there is the macro level where choices concern insurance and coverage for the population. It will include decisions regarding public or private insurance, choice of insurance organisation and the nature of the insurance plan. Next there is the meso level. This covers choices relating to providers, notably hospitals and doctors. Questions of direct access to different parts of the system are particularly important here. Finally, there is the micro level that relates to choices over particular treatments including whether, when and how treatment is provided. To what extent does choice exist over these three dimensions in other countries?

Levels and types of choice

| Macro | Meso | Micro |
|---|---|---|
| Choice whether to have health insurance | Choice of first contact provider | Choice to be treated (or right to refuse treatment) |
| Choice of public or private insurance | Choice of registered family doctor | Choice of treatment |
| Choice of insurer | Direct access to specialist | Choice of when to be treated and by whom (e.g. female doctor, midwife) |
| Choice of plan | Choice of provider:<br><br>between private and public provider<br><br>between public providers<br><br>between UK and overseas | Choice of setting:<br><br>Single room or ward<br><br>Hotel facilities<br><br>Home or hospital |
| Choice of benefits covered | Choice of specialist within hospital | Right to a second opinion |
| Choice over contribution rate | | Choice to participate in clinical trials (research) |

## Macro level

Choice at the macro level tends be high in those countries with large private insurance sectors. In the USA, for example, private health insurance is voluntary for adults under 65 who have a choice about whether to purchase insurance or not. Health insurance was also voluntary in Switzerland prior to 1996. In Germany people earning over 3,375 euros per month have a choice to opt out of the statutory health insurance (GKV). For them the decision to purchase private health insurance is also voluntary. However, once they have opted out of the statutory system it is hard to re-enter, thus this choice does not remain open to them. For individuals purchasing private insurance there is usually free choice of insurer. However where insurance is purchased by an employer on behalf of employees, there may be little or no choice of insurer and only limited plan options.

Choice of insurer also exists in the social insurance systems in Belgium, Netherlands (since 1993), Germany (since 1996) and Switzerland. Prior to 1996 in Germany, blue collar workers were assigned membership on the basis of their occupation and where they lived. In the Netherlands, membership was assigned to regional funds on the basis of place of residence prior to the introduction of competition in 1993. Private insurance companies will usually offer a range of plans with different deductibles, different benefit packages at different premia, thus offering considerable choice to the consumer. Within most social health insurance systems, the plans and benefits are standardised. However, in Switzerland consumers may opt for managed care plans or for plans with higher deductibles (and lower premia). Contribution rates vary between funds in Germany, and in the Netherlands the per capita premium levied directly by the funds also varies. In Switzerland, each insurer is free to set a community rated premium within a canton.

## Meso level

Many countries are also able to offer considerable choice at the meso level. In Sweden, for example, choice is offered in relation to the first contact provider e.g. between doctors in public health centres, outpatient clinics at hospitals or private practitioners. In countries such as Denmark, Italy, Portugal, Spain and the Netherlands where patients must register with a family doctor, patients may choose their GP (usually within geographical limits). In Austria, Belgium, Finland, France, Germany, Greece, Sweden and Switzerland and for particular groups in Denmark, patients have a choice to go straight to a specialist (without referral). In France and Sweden, initiatives have been introduced to try and increase the gate-keeping function of the generalist doctors and provide incentives to patients to first visit a primary care physician. In the Netherlands, patients receive a referral from the primary care physician to a specialty and may recommend a particular specialist but patients are free to consult the specialist of their choice.

Choice of public hospital provider exists in Denmark and Sweden. However in Sweden this varies between county councils. In Denmark, this policy was introduced in an effort to reduce waiting times and was implemented through agreements between county councils to ensure that the money followed the patient. However only 2 per cent of non acute admissions are handled under this scheme with most patients continuing to choose hospitals within the county council. Where there is a diversity of providers, choice of provider may allow patients to choose between public and private providers. Indeed in Germany and France where there is a mix of public, private not for profit and for profit hospitals patients may not even be aware of the status of the hospital with other factors having a greater influence on choice. Cross border flows of patients have always been more common in continental Europe simply due to the geography. Thus bilateral agreements already existed between neighbouring countries for the reimbursement of services provided to non resident populations. In the Netherlands which has had problems with shortage of capacity and long waiting lists, sickness funds have proactively contracted with overseas providers such as those in Belgium.

## Micro level

Finally at the micro level there are a number of important choices which centre around the patients right to determine their own treatment. First, there is the right for an adult of sound mind to refuse treatment. This is enshrined in law by most European legislatures. Second if there are multiple treatment options for a particular disorder, patients may wish to be given the right to determine this, with advice from health care professionals. Where treatments are excluded from public reimbursement or strict clinical guidelines apply, the autonomy of patients and practitioners may be reduced. For this reason financial penalties for non compliance with guidelines were fiercely opposed in France. Third, but perhaps less fundamental is the ability to choose when to be treated. In Germany most patients can be admitted to hospital the same day as the referral is made, even for treatments that would be considered elective in the UK. Unfortunately other information about systems of booked appointments overseas are not available although where waiting times are lower this may be less of an issue. Finally, a patient should be allowed, based on informed consent, to decide whether or not to participate in clinical trials. It should be made clear if particular treatment alternatives are still experimental. This is an ethical principle adhered to in most European countries.

## What choice exists in the NHS and how can it be extended?

The NHS provides health insurance coverage for all people normally resident in the country. Finance is provided through tax and national insurance contributions and there is no opportunity to opt out. As such there is no real choice at the macro level, either in terms of the decision to take out insurance or over the insurance organisation that providers the cover. Some choice is available to those that have private insurance coverage (approximately 11 per cent of the population), but this is almost invariably supplementary to the NHS not a substitute for it. Macro choice only really exists at the margins.

Critics of the lack of choice at the macro level within the NHS have contrasted the situation with social insurance countries such as Germany and the Netherlands where insurees increasingly have choice between insurance funds that purchase on their behalf. Purchasing in England is to be carried out by primary care trusts. Patients are unable to choose between PCTs. These have geographically defined catchment areas and patients who live in these areas are automatically assigned to the relevant PCT. PCTs have a spatial monopoly as purchasers.

Of course not everyone is bothered by the lower level of choice offered by PCTs. As in the Nordic countries some limitation on choice is the price that is paid for population based approaches to health care and co-ordinated service provision. In these systems patient 'voice' (representation and influence through the political and/or administrative process) is substituted for patient 'exit' (freedom to move from one provider to another as in a market) as a driver of patient-responsive services. But despite the considerable effort put into the establishment of PCT boards, with lay members who are meant to be representative of their local communities, there is still something of a democratic deficit compared with the Nordic experience.

As far as the meso level is concerned, most patient contacts in the NHS start and end with the general practice. As such choice in this area is important. Formally, the right to choose a medical practitioner is defined in the National Health Service (Primary Care) Act 1997. This choice is subject to the GP's consent and the limits placed on the maximum list size. In practice, most people register with a GP within the area in which they live and only change when they move house. With the growth of group practices, personal GP lists are becoming less common within a practice. Nonetheless, most people can generally choose to see a particular GP within a practice.

General practice has gone through a series of major reforms in recent years. The GP contract introduced in 1990 had as one of its stated aims the provision of more information and patient choice. The proportion of GPs' income paid through capitation payments was also increased, thereby offering greater incentives for GPs to attract and register patients. The subsequent development of GP fundholding and its variants strengthened the consumer focus.

This emphasis is planned to continue through primary care trusts. Each PCT will be expected to provide an independently validated annual Patient Prospectus setting out choices of services - such as the availability of female GPs or specialist services - as well as information on the availability and quality of local health services. At the same time, direct access to services through telephone advice lines such as NHS Direct is set to expand along with the establishment of 750 primary care one-stop shops.

Meso choice in relation to the secondary sector has traditionally been far more limited in the NHS. GPs acting as gatekeepers have played a pivotal role in referring patients to secondary care and have generally made decisions about choice of hospitals and consultants. These decisions have usually meant referral to the local district general hospital or, in some cases, to consultants with whom GPs have a personal relationship. Direct access to specialists is not available except in the case of accident and emergency services and some specialised services such as those relating to sexually transmitted diseases.

The internal market reforms of the 1990s were supposed to increase patient choice as health authority purchasers placed contracts with competing hospitals. In fact few areas had effective competition between hospitals and most contracts were placed with local hospitals. Perversely this meant that choice was often restricted even more than previously as GPs were required to refer patients to hospitals with whom their host district had placed a contract. Exceptions had to be dealt with under a system of extra contractual referrals whereby prior health authority authorisation was required before a patient could be treated at a non-contracted hospital. Only in the case of fundholding were GPs free to refer patients to hospitals of their choosing. There is some evidence that this reaped gains for patients in terms of shorter waiting times.[4]

Proposals set out in *The NHS Plan* and *Delivering the NHS Plan* envisage a major extension of choice in relation to secondary care. From 1 July 2002 patients waiting for more than six months for heart surgery have been offered the choice of receiving treatment at alternative providers if they can offer quicker treatment. These providers could be other NHS hospitals, private hospitals or even overseas hospitals. A pilot scheme has already been run whereby patients received surgical treatment in France and Germany in the case of ophthalmology and orthopaedic conditions. Initial evaluations indicated high levels of patient satisfaction although there were some difficulties with travel and after care. Within the UK, electronic booking of patient hospital appointments - at a time and place of their choosing - is planned to be in operation across the NHS by 2005. Choices are to be bolstered by the publication of regularly updated information on the internet of waiting lists for all major treatments at all providers.

The final aspect of meso level choice concerns decisions that take place following hospital discharge. The Government is currently concerned to ensure that the most effective use is made of acute hospital beds by making sure that patients do not remain in hospital any longer than is clinically necessary. This frequently happens when an elderly patient does not have the necessary social or nursing support to enable a discharge home to take place and/or when appropriate nursing home facilities are not available. To address this problem, extra NHS funding has been allocated to step-down, intermediate care facilities to enable patients to be discharged to less nursing-intensive care beds in non-hospital settings. More recently, the Government has also proposed a charging system whereby social service departments that fail to find residential or nursing home places for patients that are ready for hospital discharge will be fined. While the desire to make the most cost effective use of scarce hospital capacity is understandable, retaining an element of choice and autonomy for these patients will be important. A policy that aims to shunt old and frequently confused people around (people who are dubbed impersonally as 'bed blockers') must raise concerns about the levels of choice these patients are to be offered.

Choice at the micro level covers a range of aspects of care that the NHS has not traditionally been very good at providing. Frequently the service has been characterised by paternalistic providers and compliant patients. But things are changing. Increasing levels of information possessed by patients through access to, for example, the internet and the growth of consumerist attitudes are making patients far more knowledge-able and assertive. There is an increasing recognition that choices have to be made in the treatment of many diseases and disabilities, and that the patient should be a partner, alongside the clinician, in making these choices rather than a passive recipient. The Government's current plans seem to go with the grain of this cultural change through both enhanced choice and strategies for patient empowerment.

## Impact of choice

We claimed earlier that few people would argue against the provision of more choice in the NHS. Choice is usually considered a good thing per se. Among economists in particular the expression of consumer choice is viewed as the way to achieve an optimum allocation resources. But we should be aware that choice can also have some negative consequences.

The expression of effective choice requires individuals to be well informed about the costs and consequences of their decisions. We have already explained how the Government is launching major new initiatives to improve the level of patient information. But there are limits to how far this can go. Health care will remain a complex service in which the provider is always likely to have better information than the patient, especially as new technologies and extended forms of treatment come on stream. Indeed some dissenting economists have gone so far as to argue that choice can sometimes reduce an individual's utility when the costs of obtaining and processing information become too high. As such, the simple market model in which well-informed consumers express their preferences through purchasing services from providers will be of limited application in health care. Instead efforts will need to be made to develop appropriate principal-agent relationships, where the principal (the patient) is able to get the agent (doctor or other provider) to work on his or her behalf. Fortunately the well-developed GP system provides a vehicle for developing this agency function in the UK.

Another vexed question concerns choice and the private sector. At present patients who are dissatisfied with options offered by the NHS can opt for private treatment either financed through private insurance or directly out-of-pocket payments. Private treatment typically buys the services of a consultant (rather than a junior doctor) at a time of the patient's choosing in hospitals with a higher standard of hotel facilities. But the opportunity to express this choice is not evenly distributed throughout the population. Access to private treatment is related to ability to pay and is therefore taken up primarily by higher income groups. As such choice offered through private treatment can be argued to be inequitable. Moreover, because private treatment is generally provided by NHS consultants, some critics argue that it reduces their availability to the NHS thereby lengthening waiting times for NHS patients. These aspects of private healthcare demonstrate a general proposition: choice is often increased at the expense of equality. This is yet another difficult balancing act that the government will need to get right as it pursues the possibly conflicting objectives of reducing inequality and increasing choice.

## The way forward

We believe that the Government is right to seek to increase the responsiveness of the NHS to patients' needs and preferences. Much of this will be achieved through greater patient empowerment and the clearer expression of patient 'voice'. The establishment of statutorily independent Patient Forums in each Trust to monitor and review the quality of local services will be an important component of this strategy. But the Government is also right to go beyond this collective approach and to seek to offer more choice to individuals. Old style 'take-it-or-leave-it' attitudes are no longer acceptable. Offering more choice within a better-funded NHS will improve patient satisfaction and will also be a means of discouraging exit to the private sector. But there are dangers. As we have argued, processing complex information about health care is not easy. Some groups will be better placed to do this and to take advantage of choice than others. The mantra of choice should not be allowed to undermine the fundamental equity principles of the NHS. For this reason we believe that careful evaluation of the impact of programmes offering more choice, including equity audits, should form a part of the Government's approach.

# 5| Plurality and the private sector

One of the most surprising aspects of the *Delivering the NHS Plan* agenda is the proposal for more plurality and diversity through constructive engagement with the private sector. As recently as 1997, *Renewing the NHS: Labour's agenda for a healthier Britain* was deeply critical of the role of the private sector. Spending money in the private sector was claimed to undermine NHS planning and divert money into private profits and away from patient care. Now this has all changed. *The NHS Plan* argues that no ideological or institutional barriers should stand in the way of providing better care for NHS patients. It talks about partnerships with the private sector to harness its capacity to treat more NHS patients. How exactly is this intended to happen?

The Government's policy towards the private sector has two main strands; namely, an extension of the private finance initiative in relation to capital projects in both secondary and primary care, and an increased role for private sector providers of NHS funded clinical services. We consider each of these in turn.

## The Private Finance Initiative

The Private Finance Initiative (PFI) draws upon private sector finance and management expertise in order to finance, build, operate and manage NHS capital projects, particularly new hospitals. The origins of the scheme date back to 1992. Until the early 1990s, the conventional way of funding NHS capital expenditure was through Treasury finance. That is, money raised by the central government was allocated to health authorities to fund hospital building programmes and other capital projects. At the time it was argued that public finance was more cost effective because the lower risk associated with the public sector meant that it was able to raise funds more cheaply than the private sector. It also, of course, gave the Treasury direct control over this item of public expenditure.

In 1992, this situation changed quite fundamentally when the Conservative Government first sought to draw on private finance for NHS capital projects through the PFI. Under the PFI, private consortia are expected to design, finance and build projects, and also to run and maintain the non-clinical services over the lifetime of the agreement. The facilities are then leased back to the public sector for an annual rental payment, typically over a 30 year period. In 1994 the government introduced the requirement that all NHS organisations were to explore PFI options initially and only if private finance was not available, would exchequer finance be considered.

Despite the considerable emphasis placed upon the PFI in ministerial speeches over the period 1992-97, various legislative and administrative obstacles meant that no schemes actually came on stream during that period. It was when the new Labour Government came to office in 1997 that the scheme really took off. By the end of 2000, 23 major PFI contracts had been signed. In February 2001, the Secretary of State announced another 29 schemes with an estimated capital value of £3.1 billion. In February 2002, a PFI scheme at Barts and The London NHS Trust with a total capital cost of £620 million was announced, making it the largest capital scheme in the NHS to date. The scheme will provide 1285 beds and is expected to come on stream in phases over the next ten years. In total, the PFI currently provides more than 85 per cent of capital funding for major new NHS projects. By 2003/04, the PFI is expected to account for 22.2 per cent of total NHS capital expenditure in England.

Delivering the NHS Plan proposes the extension of PFI to other parts of the health and social care system. These will include major new investments in primary care facilities, upgrading mental and community health facilities and generally assisting the shift of balance from hospital-based care to care in community settings.

The official case for the PFI has been framed in terms of both macro and micro economic benefits. The macro economic case centres on the ability to raise finance privately that cannot be raised publicly because of public expenditure constraints. Substituting private for public finance is seen as a way of taking expenditure out of the public accounts at a time when considerable emphasis is placed upon the need to contain public expenditure.

As far as micro economic policy is concerned, the involvement of the private sector is seen as spur to efficiency in a similar way to that in which general privatisation policy has been viewed. Government economists argue that the process can improve value-for-money in a number of ways. These include a better allocation of risk between the public and private sectors; better incentives to perform as payments are linked directly to contractor's performance; closer integration of service needs with design and construction; the promotion of maximum efficiency in the use of assets over the long term; ensuring that assets are fully fit for purpose, i.e. avoiding the historical tendency to over provide; and economies of scale through larger projects.

Set against these arguments, there have been a number of criticisms of the PFI programme. At the macro level, the claim that

59

PFI generates additional investment finance to that which would have been available through Exchequer funding has been challenged. Although it might seem this way to a hard pressed NHS manager, it has been argued that shortages of public funding arise solely from government-imposed cash constraints and that the same resources are used over the lifetime of a project no matter whether projects are funded publicly or privately.

At the micro level, the main debate surrounds the impact of PFI on efficiency: that is, does the PFI lead to lower costs and/or higher quality of services than conventional procurement? This question has been examined in relation to three main aspects of the PFI process; namely, the design, construction and provision of non clinical services over the duration of a project.

The pro-PFI case on design is that it permits the application of private sector innovation and creativity. In fact, risk aversion has probably led to less innovation in PFI schemes than are found in schemes designed through traditional methods. As far as construction is concerned, it is argued by advocates of PFI that private sector discipline avoids time and cost overruns. In fact, something of a myth has grown up around the scale of public sector cost overruns, and in fact they have been rather modest.[5] PFI may have made NHS managers more aware of risk management, but once this lesson has been learned it can be applied equally to conventional publicly funded projects. Finally, has the provision of non-clinical services (e.g. maintenance, portering, domestic services) been undertaken more efficiently under a PFI scheme? There is currently no direct evidence on this question. There is, however, considerable evidence on sub-contracting of non-clinical services in the NHS during the 1980s and 1990s and this evidence is mixed in its support of private sector options.[6]

An additional cost associated with PFI arises because of the uncertainty associated with the demand for services from a particular asset over a 30 year period. Long term contracts are particularly problematic where technological change can have a major impact on the efficient configuration of assets. If demand falls for an asset at a particular location, or offering a particular configuration of services, a PFI agreement may mean that the public sector is locked into a long term agreement even though changed circumstances mean that the asset is no longer required. Under a conventional public sector funding option, closure of the facility would be less costly, although it may encounter more political opposition.

In addition to the expansion of the PFI in the hospital sector, the government aims to draw on private sector funding for substantial investment in primary care. In November 2001, the Secretary of State announced new types of private investment in GPs surgeries as part of a £55 million package. These will involve a £10 million investment through six NHS Local Improvement Finance Trusts (LIFT) projects. NHS LIFT is a new public-private partnership (50 per cent owned by the Department of Health and 50 per cent by Partnerships UK) that will build and refurbish GP premises and then lease them to GPs. Initially it will concentrate its efforts in areas of greatest need where premises are in the poorest condition, and where there is a pressing need to attract younger GPs.

The Government has a clear commitment to the modernisation of primary care. It sees the provision of integrated and accessible services, offering 'one stop' care, as a key part of its modernisation programme. At the moment there are too few primary care premises capable of housing an extended and comprehensive range of services. A recent research study of Primary Care Groups indicated that over 60 per cent of them saw investment in their premises as a high or very high priority and 72 per cent said that they have at least one practice where premises fall below minimum standards. The Government sees private finance as having a role to play in addressing these problems.

There is, at the moment, little evaluative evidence enabling an assessment of the performance of public-private partnerships in this area.

Clearly greater private sector participation in primary care has made available higher levels of investment funding than were likely to be made available through purely public funding. But, as in the hospital sector, part of the explanation for differential levels of funding is likely to be attributable to tight public expenditure constraints that are not applied to the private sector. Unlike the hospital case though, entrepreneurial private sector activity may have acted as a greater stimulus to investment in primary care. To this extent, it represents a net addition to overall investment rather than substitution between the private and public sectors.

Set against this possible advantage, however, there are a number of potential risks of PFIs in primary care. Fears have been expressed about GPs over-extending themselves and for future loan payments drawing on monies that should be used for funding clinical services. Inflexible long term contracts also pose problems. In addition, accounts of two case studies of public-private, primary care partnerships in the North of England raise concerns about the workload and management time involved in putting together public-private partnership deals and the possibility of a power imbalance between public and private sector negotiators.

## Public Private Partnerships

The second main area of activity involving the NHS and the private sector centres on the private provision of publicly funded services for NHS patients through public private partnerships (PPPs). Although the concept of a PPP is frequently seen as a modern one, it is important to realise that different forms of public-private relationship were built into the fabric of the UK health system from the start of the NHS. GPs working as independent contractors, NHS pay beds, hospital consultants working in both the NHS and private sectors, and joint working between the NHS and the pharmaceutical industry are all long-standing examples of this dual relationship.

It was, however, during the 1990s that the current version of this relationship started to emerge. A constant theme of government micro economic policy in the previous decade had been a belief in the superior efficiency of the private sector. A central component of this belief was that it was the competitive environment within which private sector firms operated that provided the necessary incentive structure for increased efficiency. Building on these beliefs, the 1991 NHS reforms introduced a market-like structure to the NHS in which the responsibility for purchasing services was separated from the responsibility for providing them.

As part of these reforms, the Government wished to see district health authorities and GP fundholders purchasing services from both public and private sector providers. It was envisaged that the private sector would play an increased role in the provision of publicly funded services through the extension of competitive tendering for support services; encouraging joint ventures between the public and private sectors, especially in relation to capital projects; and as NHS purchasers bought clinical services for NHS patients from the private sector.

In fact, the development of pluralism in the supply of clinical services during the period of the internal market (1991-97) was very limited. Most purchasing and providing took place between NHS organisations. There was some intersectoral trade but this was usually at the margins involving, for example, specialised forms of provision (e.g. psychiatric care) or short term initiatives (e.g. policies aimed at reductions in waiting lists). There was also some purchasing from the private sector undertaken by GP fundholders but, again, the volumes of activity were relatively small. It is worth noting, however, that this experience of limited use of the private sector was in stark contrast to the social care sector where there was a massive expansion of publicly financed, privately provided services.

As we pointed out earlier, one might have expected that the election of a Labour government in 1997 would have signalled the demise of PPPs. While in opposition the party had been scathing about the role of the private sector and the threat posed by privatisation. Certainly during the early years of the new Labour Government there was little appetite for greater private sector involvement in the provision of clinical services, beyond helping out with short term pressures.

But this situation is now changing quite markedly and rapidly. In October 2000, an event of considerable significance occurred when the Secretary of State for Health signed a concordat with the Independent Healthcare Association. The concordat established the parameters for a completely new partnership approach between the NHS and private and voluntary sector providers of health care. It is based on the premise that there should be no organisational or ideological barriers to the delivery of high quality health care free at the point of delivery. The approach clearly draws on the general new Labour belief that the private sector has relevant skills that can improve the efficiency of the public sector.

Interest in drawing on private sector capacity has undoubtedly been stimulated by the need for the NHS to deal with winter pressures for hospital admissions. Shortage of NHS beds at peak periods of demand has led to severe difficulties in recent years. Moreover, meeting NHS Plan targets in relation to waiting times and other indicators of performance has led to a need for a rapid increase in resources available to the NHS. However, the concordat envisages moving beyond short term co-operation to longer-term service agreements. Early concordat initiatives have focused on two main service areas - elective care and intermediate care.

In the case of elective care, government guidance has suggested that a primary care trust could commission or rent facilities from the private sector with the actual service being provided by NHS doctors and other staff under an NHS contract. Alternatively an NHS acute hospital trust could sub-contract the provision of some services to the private sector. In other cases a primary care trust might decide to commission services directly from the private sector. *Delivering the NHS Plan* estimates that up to 150,000 operations per year might be bought from the private sector for NHS patients.

Intermediate care is a policy area that has been received considerable attention in its own right. It covers a range of services designed to promote independence among patients by avoiding unnecessary hospital admissions, avoiding unnecessarily long lengths of hospital stay by enabling timely discharge from hospital, promoting effective rehabilitation programmes and planning new services in non-acute hospital environments such as community hospitals, hospital-at-home schemes. Intermediate care policy is seen as particularly important in the case of increasing numbers of elderly people who are often admitted to acute hospitals, and remain there unnecessarily, because of a lack of suitable facilities. As such the Government has allocated £900 million over the period until 2003/04 for its development. This is expected to generate an additional 5,000 intermediate care beds by this date. The Government sees the private sector as a valuable source of additional capacity in view of the need to develop intermediate care facilities rapidly. Companies such as BUPA homes are already established providers in this market and are currently seeking to expand their activities in this area.

In the two years since the signing of the concordat a whole raft of policy statements reinforcing the emphasis on a joint public-private approach have appeared. These have included announcements about major NHS contracts placed with private hospitals; the prospect of the management of failing NHS hospitals being franchised to private sector managers; setting up specialist diagnostic and treatment centres; and the partnering of primary care trusts with experienced international commissioning organisations. In this latter case, ministers and officials have held talks with the US managed care organisation, Kaiser Permanente, about offering assistance to PCTs, and another US company, United Healthcare, has started to work with PCTs on a pilot basis to assist them in setting up information systems.

There have also been initiatives involving overseas providers. A pilot scheme involving the treatment of NHS patients in French and German hospitals has taken place. A recent Department of Health prospectus has been issued setting out the terms for inviting overseas providers to the NHS to increase surgical and diagnostic capacity. It is envisaged that they may run some of the new diagnostic and treatment centres. Campaigns for the international recruitment of doctors are also underway. The Department of Health has set up an international establishment programme to co-ordinate and manage this activity.

Looked at overall, the concordat and associated PPP initiatives represent a fundamental change in the way that the NHS is expected to work with the private sector. Despite strong ministerial commitment, however, progress on the ground seems to have been slow. NHS expenditure in the private sector is still less than one percent of total acute spending. Many private sector organisations report a reluctance of NHS managers to enter into longer-term, working relationships and claim that collaboration is still mainly driven by short term needs.

## Assessment of the changing public private mix

Much of the political debate surrounding the role of the private sector in relation to health care is dominated by values and ideology. The government wishes to move away from this agenda and takes the view that what is important is what works. We broadly share this view but believe that it begs the question: what works? Put another way: the main unanswered questions concerning private sector involvement in health care are empirical ones, namely, what is the relative performance of the public and private sectors in terms of key criteria such as efficiency, equity, quality of care, public health, transparency and accountability?

In the case of PFI, most serious commentators accept that the case in terms of macro efficiency (reduced public expenditure) is a spurious one. The case in terms of micro efficiency is less clear cut, although there are numerous reasons for questioning the official case for the policy. Transparency is not helped by the fact that commercial confidentiality makes it very difficult for independent analysts to analyse the relative costs and benefits of PFI investments. The House of Commons Select Committee on Health recently took the view that many questions remain to be answered about the wisdom of pursuing the PFI programme. They called for more capital monies to be made available for conventionally procured schemes so that PFI could then be properly monitored against them. We share this view and regret that the government has not accepted this recommendation.

Far less analytical attention has to date been focused on the private provision of NHS funded clinical services. In part, this is because the scale of activity is still very small. But activity is clearly increasing rapidly in this area. Our view is that encouragement of greater plurality on the supply-side is worthwhile as an exploratory strategy. We believe this because of the general undesirability of monopoly provision - partly on the grounds of lack of responsiveness to users and partly because of the spur to efficiency offered by competition and contestability from independent providers. On the other hand, we are concerned about the rapid development of policy in this area when so many questions remain about relative public-private sector cost effectiveness, uneven quality assurance mechanisms, the greater complexity of partnership working when private sector organisations are involved and a yet-to-be-tested regulatory regime. We also recognise that there are legitimate concerns about the pay and working conditions for erstwhile public sector workers as well as possible threats to 'public sector values' when the private sector assumes responsibility for the provision of services. These uncertainties require much closer attention to be paid to evaluation so that evidence on performance can be assembled before the policy is rolled out on a larger scale.

# 6| Conclusion

The central message of this report is distinctly undramatic. We are not calling for a headline grabbing fundamental reform of the UK health service. Far from it. In our view, there have been far too many 'big ideas' floating around in recent years. These have had led to constant re-disorganisation of the NHS and performance has suffered. We believe that the time has come for consolidation and development within a more stable environment.

We reject the calls for new forms of health finance. The ideas involving hypothecation, social insurance and a greater role for private funding have been around for years and have been subjected to endless scrutiny. Almost all serious commentators question the advantages they offer over the current central tax-based system of finance. The one possible advantage that such systems offer, namely the capacity to deliver more generous levels of funding, has been put firmly on the back-burner by the Chancellor's spending plans for the period up to 2008. These are planned to raise spending on health care to over 9 per cent of GDP and defuse the case for additional sources of funding, at least in the medium term.

The challenges facing the UK health system for the remainder of the decade will almost certainly surround the supply-side. In particular, how should increased funding be used to improve the quantity and quality of health care provision? Once again we do not favour going back to first principles and redesigning the organisation and management of the health care system once again. On the contrary, we believe that the agenda set out by the government in *The NHS Plan* and *Delivering the NHS Plan* represents a workable framework for the future development of the NHS. On the other hand, there are a number of aspects of this agenda that require clarification, adjustment and refinement. We have concentrated on some of these aspects in this report.

As far as the allocation of funding is concerned, we are disappointed that public health has slipped down the political agenda and would urge ministers to concentrate on health and not simply health care. We recognise the major contributions to the furtherance of evidence-based practice in terms of clinical and cost effectiveness represented by the work of the National Institute of Clinical Excellence and the development of National Service Frameworks, but are concerned by the implementation gap. This applies particularly in relation to the work of NICE where a science-led approach has failed to address the social and political implications of the Institute's recommendations, and the task of securing the support of individual clinicians. These shortcomings need to be addressed. We further believe that greater explicitness about NHS entitlements would assist the process of rational resource allocation.

We recognise that the existence of a National Health Service and the political accountability of the Secretary of State for the performance of the NHS to Parliament means that a degree of central direction and control will always be a feature of the heath system. But we are concerned about the degree of intervention being exerted at the moment. We believe that the proper role of government is in the stewardship of the system and that this involves steering not rowing. Governments have a history of failing to let go. Local innovation and enthusiasm is stifled if managers are deluged with central guidance, directives and targets. Effort is diverted to managing upwards rather than managing local organisations downwards. Genuine service change is forfeited in the quest to meet national must-dos. We believe that the government needs to place more confidence in local decision makers rather than less. Put bluntly, the government needs to curb its interventionist tendencies and steer with a lighter touch.

Policy towards foundation hospitals provides a good example of this requirement. We recognise some of the dangers posed by this initiative but, on balance, believe that the provision of more autonomy and local responsiveness is to be encouraged. Any additional turbulence will obviously need to be managed, but central regulation should not be so strong as to negate the potential advantages of more local freedom. We believe that initiatives designed to increase patient choice in the NHS are long overdue. For too long NHS patients have been offered a 'take it or leave it' service. Restricted choice in the NHS has contrasted quite vividly with the wider range of choice offered to patients in many other European health care systems. For this reason, we welcome the Government's commitment to extending choice. However, we believe that there needs to be far greater recognition of the different dimensions of patient choice and their impact upon both patients and the NHS. Choice can only be meaningful if patients have access to accurate and timely information. Most patient decisions will continue to be made in consultation with GPs and hospital doctors and nurses. Mechanisms for facilitating joint decision making need to be nurtured. There will also be occasions when greater choice may threaten other NHS objectives, including those relating to equity of access. These trade-offs need to be confronted - the mantra of choice should not be allowed to undermine fundamental NHS principles.

The extension of choice is closely related to the encouragement of a more diverse and pluralist delivery system, involving both the public and private sectors. Given the governments well-publicised earlier aversion to private sector involvement with the NHS, their current policy direction represents something of a U-turn. We believe that as long as the equity objectives of the NHS are met through public funding, there are good arguments for encouraging diversity of suppliers. Competition and contestability can provide the necessary incentive structure for greater efficiency and more responsiveness to patients, if developed properly. But at the same time we have to concede that much policy in this area proceeds on the basis of ideology and a priori assertion. Given the total absence of empirical evidence on even such basic features as the relative cost effectiveness of public and private sector provision, we believe that there is an over-whelming case for more monitoring and evaluation to be carried out in this area in order to inform future policy decisions.

None of these proposals amount to a revolution. As we have made clear throughout this report, we believe that this is the last thing that the NHS needs at the present time. In our view a workable programme has been set out in *Delivering the NHS Plan*. What is now required is calibration of this programme, not more new initiatives or reorganisations. Put another way: the avoid-ance of more turbulence and greater continuity through evidence-based development within a stable policy environment.

# Appendix | Health Policy Forum seminars

*Health Policy Forum opening lecture*
Alan Milburn MP (Secretary of State for Health)

*Financing the NHS: Is a hypothecated health tax the answer?*
Speakers included Frank Dobson MP (former Secretary of State for Health) and Sir Nick Monck (former Second Permanent Secretary, HM Treasury)

*Financing the NHS: Is there a European social insurance model?*
Speakers included Dr Howard Stoate MP, Reinhard Busse (Head of the Madrid Hub, European Health Observatory) and Anna Dixon ( LSE)

*Moral dilemmas over rationing*
Speakers included Konrad Obermann (German Technical Corporation) and J Michael Leahy (former Director of Oregon Community Health Organisation)

*The comparative value of investing money in different areas*
Speakers included Professor Alan Maynard (University of York) and Dan Mendelson (formerly Office of Management and Budget, White House)

# Completing the Course

*Is prevention better than treatment?*
Speakers included Professor Alistair Hall (Leeds University), David Woodhead (Kings Fund) and Bruce Vladeck (former Administrator for US Medicare)

*Patient choice*
Speakers included Mike Hall MP (PPS to Alan Milburn), Nicholas Bromley (Centre for Reform) and Jeanne Lambrew, (George Washington University)

*Inequalities in healthcare delivery*
Speakers included Hazel Blears MP (Health Minister), Adam Olive, (LSE) and Jack Lew (former Director, Office of Management and Budget, White House)

# References

1.  *User charges for health care. Funding health care: options for Europe* R Robinson, Open University Press, 2001
2.  The Erosion of Employer-Based Health Coverage and the Threat to Workers. Health Care Findings from The Commonwealth Fund 2002 Workplace Health Insurance Survey. Available at www.cmwf.org
3.  Peter Smith, personal communication.
4.  *GPs and purchasing in the NHS: the internal market and beyond,* B Dowling, Ashgate, 2000
5.  *The economics of the private finance initiative in the NHS* J Sussex, Office of Health Economics, 2001
6.  *To market, to market*, W Ranade, National Association of Health Authorities, 1989

## Bibliography

### Introduction

*The NHS Plan: a plan for investment, a plan for reform*, Department of Health , 2000, www.doh.gov.uk/nhsplan

*Delivering the NHS Plan: next steps on investment, next steps on reform*, Department of Health, 2002, www.doh.gov.uk/deliveringthenhsplan

'Raising the Money', G Brown, HM Treasury, 2002, www.hm-treasury.gov.uk

*The inconsistencies of the National Health Service*, J Buchanan, Institute of Economic Affairs, 1965

*Paying for Progress: A New Politics of Tax for Public Spending, Report of the  Commission on Taxation and Citizenship*, Fabian Society, 2000

'Funding the NHS. Is the NHS underfunded?', British Medical Journal 314(7073), J Dixon,  A Harrison and B New, 1997

*Future health care options*, T Ensor, The Institute for Health Services Management, 1993

*Funding health care: options for Europe*, E Mossialos, A Dixon, J Figueras, et al,  Open University Press, 2002

'Securing our future health: taking a long-term view: interim report', D Wanless, HM Treasury, 2001, www.hm-treasury.gov.uk/wanless

'Securing our future health: taking a long-term view: final report' D Wanless, HM Treasury, 2002, www.hm-treasury.gov.uk/wanless

### Investing wisely

'Independent inquiry into inequalities in health report', D Acheson, Department of Health, 1998

'Healthcare funding review', BMA Health Policy and Economic Research Unit , 2001, www.bma.org.uk

'About the Commission for Health Improvement', Commission for Health Improvement, 2002, www.chi.nhs.uk

'Wrong SIGN, NICE mess: is national guidance distorting allocation of resources?', R Cookson, D McDaid and A Maynard, British Medical

Journal 323(7315), 2001

National Service Frameworks, Department of Health, 2002, www.doh.gov.uk/nsf/

*Public Health: the Vision and the Challenge*, W W Holland and S Stewart, Nuffield Trust, 1998

*Managing scarcity: priority setting and rationing in the NHS*, R Klein, Open University Press, 1996

'A Guide to Our Work', National Institute for Clinical Excellence, 2002, www.nice.org.uk


National standards versus local autonomy

*NHS Foundation Trusts: Eligibility Criteria and Timetable*, Department of Health, 2002

*Reforming markets in health care: an economic perspective*, MGoddard, R Mannion and P Smith, Open University Press, 2000

*The politics of NHS reform 1988-97*, C Ham, King's Fund, 2000

*Learning from the NHS internal market,*J Grand, N Mays and J Mulligan, King's Fund, 1998

'Beware the boomerang policy', A Maynard, Health Service Journal, 112: 18, 2002

*The purchasing of health care by primary care organizations: an evaluation and guide to future policy*, N Mays, S Wyke, G Malbon and N Goodwin (eds), Open University Press, 2001

'NHS foundation hospitals', R Robinson, British Medical Journal 325: 506-7, 2002

*Implementing planned markets in health care*, R Saltman and C von Otter, Open University Press, 1995


Choices in health care

'Extending choice for patients: A discussion document. Proposals for pilot schemes to improve choice and provide faster treatment' , Department of Health., 2001, www.doh.gov.uk/extendingchoice

*Health Care Systems in Eight Countries: Trends and Challenges*, A Dixon and E Mossialos (eds), European Observatory on Health Care Systems, 2002, www.observatory.dk

'Managed competition: an agenda for action', A C Enthoven, Health Affairs (Millwood) 7(3): 25-47, 1988

'Free choice of sickness funds in regulated competition: evidence from Germany and the Netherlands', S Greß, P Groenewegen, J Kerssens et al, Health Policy 60(3): 235-54, 2002

'Evaluation of treating patients overseas: Final report', K Lowson, P West, S Chaplin et al, Department of Health, 2002, www.doh.gov.uk

'Citizens or shoppers? Solidarity under siege', J A Morone, D W Light and D Wilsford, Journal of Health Politics, Policy and Law 25(5): 959-78 and other country specific articles on competition which can be found in this special issue, 2000

*The social economics of health care,* J B Davis, Routledge, 2001

*Coercive care : the ethics of choice in health and medicine,* T Tännsjö, Routledge, 1999

Plurality and the private sector

'For the benefit of patients - a concordat with the private and voluntary health care provider sector, Guidance Note' Department of Health, 2000

'Intermediate care', Health Circular, Department of Health, 2001

*Public-private partnerships in the NHS,* D Hunter, R Robinson, B New, Nuffield Trust, 2002

*Building better partnerships: the final report of the commission on public private partnerships,* Institute for Public Policy Research, 2001

*A healthy partnership: the future of public-private partnerships in the health service,* G Kelly and P Robinson (eds), Institute for Public Policy Research

*Disease management, the NHS and the pharmaceutical industry,* J Mason, A Towse and M Drummond, Office of Health Economics, 1999

'How private finance is moving primary care into corporate ownership', A Pollock, S Player and S Godden, British Medical Journal. 322: 960-3, 2001

# Paying for Progress
## A New Politics of Tax for Public Spending

The Commission on Taxation and Citizenship

Taxation—and the public spending it pays for—is the subject of the fiercest political controversy. *Paying for Progress: A New Politics of Tax for Public Spending* offers a compelling new approach.

Reporting new research into public attitudes towards taxation, Paying for Progress argues that the public must be 'reconnected' to the taxes they pay and the public services which these finance. To do this it proposes the greater use of 'earmarked' taxes, including a new tax to fund the National Health Service. Setting out a new philosophy of citzenship to underpin taxation policy, it recommends a series of reforms to meet the goals of social inclusion and environmental protection.

Written in a lively and accessible style, *Paying for Progress* makes an important contribution to political thought and policy in the first decade of the 21st century. Providing key information on the UK tax system, it will also be an invaluable text for students and researchers in politics, economics, public administration, law and accountancy.

'Coherent, radical and lucid... this important book raises critical questions for the future of British politics'
Will Hutton, Chief Executive, the Industrial Society

'The clarity with which it explores the facts and arguments about the tax system make it an extremely valuable text for students and researchers. It will provide a benchmark for future work on taxation reform'
Andrew Gamble, Professor of Politics, University of Sheffield

November 2000 ISBN 07163 6003 9 £9.95

**Email bookshop@fabian-society.org.uk or call 020 7227 4900**

Other Fabian Society Publications

# Coping with Post-democracy

Colin Crouch

'In this stimulating new pamphlet, Professor Colin Crouch makes links between the decline of the state and the waning of democratic enthusiasm. When so much of the public sector has been handed over to private operators, Crouch argues, what becomes of the image of government as a task that matters? If every public function is tested by its conformity with private-sector management goals, why should anyone get excited about choosing between parties? If government is routinely seen as incompetent, and the company as the only source of expertise, no wonder politics and democracy, in America if not yet here, are at an all-time low. This is a fate that Labour, not so long ago, would have been desperate to avoid ... At some stage, the Labour party may have to confront the lacuna that has been created on the left.' Hugo Young, The *Guardian*

Colin Crouch is Professor of Sociology at the European University Institute, Florence, and External Scientific member of the Max Planck Institute for Society Research, Cologne

December 2000  ISBN 07163 0598 4  £6.95

**Email bookshop@fabian-society.org.uk or call 020 7227 4900**